What I Love about You, Sis

1

I love sharing

Time
____

with you.

2

You have the best

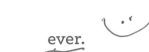

LAUGH!

ever.

3

When we were ~~little~~ younger I loved

seeing you at parties

with you.

(ok, I messed this up, but you know what I mean)

:)

4

I still want that

____

you used to have.

5

It means a lot that
you showed me how to

______________________________ .

6

I admire how you

every day.

7

I can always count on you to

______________________________ .

8

We should totally

____

again.

9

I wish we could still play

____

together.

10

I love remembering how we

____ .

11

I was always secretly jealous of your

______________________________.

12

It always makes me laugh when you

______________________________________.

13

The world seriously needs
to know about your

Awesome Writing!

14

I love when you tell me

Funny Stories ____________.
from our past
Lives & Adventures!

15

I love going

Shopping

with you.

You find the coolest stuff!

16

I used to love it when you

____ .

17

I used to hate it when you

____.

18

Your

____

is so awesome to me.

19

I love remembering when we went

____

with

_______________________________.

20

I'm so glad we got to

____.

21

You deserve the

____

award.

22

I am so

____

that

________________________________.

23

I love how you never

____.

24

I love how you always

______________________________ .

25

If I had to describe you
in one word, it'd be

____.

26

Your

____

makes me happy.

27

I'd love to borrow your

____ .

OK?

28

If you were an amusement park ride,
you'd be

___________________________________ .

29

I'd love it if we could

____

together again.

30

I love laughing about the time we

____

with

_______________________________________.

31

I hope you get to

____

your favorite

____

soon.

32

I love spending

____

with you.

33

I'm glad we didn't

____.

34

Your

cracks me up.

35

Thanks for helping me

____ .

36

Sometimes your ability to

____

amazes me.

37

I'm sorry I made you

____

that one time.

38

I'd be lost without your

______________________________ .

39

If you were a famous singer, you'd be

____ .

40

I wish I had your

____

talent.

41

Just so you know,
I totally forgive you for

____.

42

I have to admit you're
always right about

____.

43

I love how you always say,

"______________________________."

44

I still can't believe you

____

when you were

____.

45

I hope to be as

____

as you one day.

46

I love to make you

______________________________________ .

47

It was so cool of you to let me

______________________________ .

48

Nobody else can

____

like you.

49

It's sweet how you always let me

____.

50

Thanks for being so

______________________________________ .

I love you, Sis!

Created, published, and distributed by Knock Knock
1635-B Electric Ave.
Venice, CA 90291
knockknockstuff.com
Knock Knock is a registered trademark of Knock Knock LLC
Fill in the Love is a registered trademark of Knock Knock LLC

Made in China

UPC: 825703-50086-8
ISBN: 978-160106759-3

10 9 8